Future Inventor

Future Snowboarder

Future Dancer

Future Musician

Future Chef

Future Artist

Future Engineer

To my girls, Tess and Kat
who are both AWESOME! ~ C.H.

For Eloise Matthews ~ A.P.

First published in 2018 by Scholastic Children's Books

Euston House, 24 Eversholt Street, London NW1 1DB

a division of Scholastic Ltd

www.scholastic.co.uk

London ~ New York ~ Toronto ~ Sydney ~

Auckland ~ Mexico City ~ New Delhi ~ Hong Kong

1 2 3 4 5 6 7 8 9 10

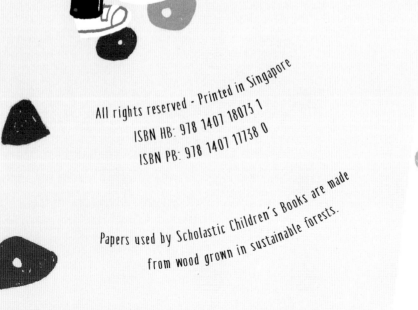

Papers used by Scholastic Children's Books are made
from wood grown in sustainable forests.

GIRLS Can Do ANYTHING

CARYL HART

ALI PYE

Girls come in all different colours and sizes.

They delight and amaze us.
They're full of surprises.

Girls can do **anything** they want to do.
And if **YOU** are a girl ...

... you can do these things too!

Girls can have **long hair**
or **short hair** in spikes.

Girls can ride **scooters**
and **skateboards** and **bikes**.

Girls can wear trousers,
or board-shorts
or dresses.

Girls can be neat ...

...or make wonderful messes.

Girls can be scruffy or
muddy and smelly.

Girls can be fancy,
like people on telly.

All girls
are different ...

...but **one** thing is true —

there's **NO** other girl on the planet like **you!**

Girls can play
basketball, football or catch,
or score lots of goals
in an ice-hockey match.

Girls can climb mountains
and other high places.

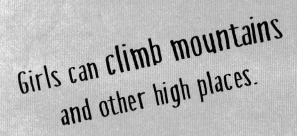

And win golden medals
in all sorts of races.

Girls are **amazing**.
So shout it out loud —

"I'm a GIRL!
I'm FANTASTIC!
I'm strong, brave and proud!"

Some girls like **numbers** and some prefer **writing**.

Some girls find **science** or **music** exciting.

Some girls are **whizzy**
with pom-poms and glue.

But all girls are
brilliant,
and that includes
you!

Now here is a secret the whole world should know,
girls get MORE awesome the older they grow.

Some help
protect tigers,

or heal
people's pets.

Some learn to be zookeepers, farmers or vets.

Girls can **drive lorries** to
haul heavy loads,

or build **fancy houses,** or **dig up the roads.**

Girls can be **brave**
like this firefighter here,
rescuing people when danger is near.

Girls can be **gentle,**

and girls can be **rough.**

You can **count** on a girl when the going gets tough.

Girls are **amazing.** So shout it out loud —

"I'm a GIRL! I'm FANTASTIC!
I'm strong, brave and proud!"

MARIE CURIE

EMMANUELLE
CHARPENTIER

CLARA BARTON

ALEXA CANADY

Now, how many girls have **invented** a way
to make people's lives a bit better each day?

ELIZABETH BLACKWELL

ROSALIND FRANKLIN

FLORENCE NIGHTINGALE

HUALAN CHEN

They've **discovered** the causes of coughs, spots and sneezes and learned how to treat many nasty diseases.

A girl can **explore** a hot jungly place,

or **float** in a rocket ship way out in space.

Girls can fly planes or dive under the sea.

Yes, girls can be ANYTHING they want to be.

A girl can find clues

to help **solve**

tricky
crimes.

Or **speak out for others**
at difficult times.

When a girl is determined, she **always** succeeds.
Her **courage** and **strength** are what everyone needs.

THE NEWS

Girls are amazing.
So shout it out loud —
"I'm a GIRL! I'm FANTASTIC!

I'm strong, brave and proud!"

And the girl I love best
in the whole world is YOU.
Dream BIG, special girl.
Tell me, what will YOU do?

Claudia Gordon — Lawyer
First deaf African American female attorney in the US

Maryam Mirzakhani — Mathematician
Winner of the Fields Medal, 2014

Arunima Sinha — Mountaineer
First female amputee to climb Mount Everest

Marin Alsop — Conductor
First female conductor at the *Last Night of the Proms*

Serena Williams — Tennis Player
Tennis champion and icon

Jane Goodall — Primatologist
Ethologist, anthropologist, and UN Messenger of Peace

Nicola Adams — Boxer
First female and openly LGBTQ person to win a boxing gold at the Olympics

Sue Wimpenny — Builder
Builder and CEO